STEIFF BEAR, 1920's

MAKE UNKNOWN

CHILTERN BEAR, 1950's

CHILTERN BEAR (English), 1930's

FARNELL BEAR (English), 1920's

MAKE UNKNOWN, c. 1915

SUE PEARSON'S
TEDDY BEAR COLLECTORS DIARY 1999

HUTCHINSON
LONDON SYDNEY AUCKLAND JOHANNESBURG

NAME . . . .

ADDRESS . . . .

. . . .

. . . .

POSTCODE . . . . TEL: . . . . FAX: . . . .

In memory of my mother, 1904 – 1997

Photographs by Roddy Paine, Guy Ryecart, Fiona Pragoff copyright © Hutchinson Children's Books,
photographs by Michael Pearson copyright © the photographer

First published in the United Kingdom in 1998 by
Hutchinson Children's Books
Random House UK Limited
20 Vauxhall Bridge Road, London SW1V 2SA

Random House Australia (Pty) Limited
20 Alfred Street, Milsons Point, Sydney
New South Wales 2061, Australia

Random House New Zealand Limited
18 Poland Road, Glenfield
Auckland 10, New Zealand

Random House South Africa (Pty) Limited
Endulini, 5A Jubilee Road, Parktown 2193, South Africa

Random House UK Registered No 954009

Printed in Singapore

ISBN: 0 09 176950 7

1999 CALENDAR

JANUARY

M	T	W	T	F	S	S
				1	2	3
4	5	6	7	8	9	10
11	12	13	14	15	16	17
18	19	20	21	22	23	24
25	26	27	28	29	30	31

FEBRUARY

M	T	W	T	F	S	S
1	2	3	4	5	6	7
8	9	10	11	12	13	14
15	16	17	18	19	20	21
22	23	24	25	26	27	28

MARCH

M	T	W	T	F	S	S
1	2	3	4	5	6	7
8	9	10	11	12	13	14
15	16	17	18	19	20	21
22	23	24	25	26	27	28
29	30	31				

APRIL

M	T	W	T	F	S	S
			1	2	3	4
5	6	7	8	9	10	11
12	13	14	15	16	17	18
19	20	21	22	23	24	25
26	27	28	29	30		

MAY

M	T	W	T	F	S	S
					1	2
3	4	5	6	7	8	9
10	11	12	13	14	15	16
17	18	19	20	21	22	23
24	25	26	27	28	29	30
31						

JUNE

M	T	W	T	F	S	S
	1	2	3	4	5	6
7	8	9	10	11	12	13
14	15	16	17	18	19	20
21	22	23	24	25	26	27
28	29	30				

JULY

M	T	W	T	F	S	S
			1	2	3	4
5	6	7	8	9	10	11
12	13	14	15	16	17	18
19	20	21	22	23	24	25
26	27	28	29	30	31	

AUGUST

M	T	W	T	F	S	S
						1
2	3	4	5	6	7	8
9	10	11	12	13	14	15
16	17	18	19	20	21	22
23	24	25	26	27	28	29
30	31					

SEPTEMBER

M	T	W	T	F	S	S
		1	2	3	4	5
6	7	8	9	10	11	12
13	14	15	16	17	18	19
20	21	22	23	24	25	26
27	28	29	30			

OCTOBER

M	T	W	T	F	S	S
				1	2	3
4	5	6	7	8	9	10
11	12	13	14	15	16	17
18	19	20	21	22	23	24
25	26	27	28	29	30	31

NOVEMBER

M	T	W	T	F	S	S
1	2	3	4	5	6	7
8	9	10	11	12	13	14
15	16	17	18	19	20	21
22	23	24	25	26	27	28
29	30					

DECEMBER

M	T	W	T	F	S	S
		1	2	3	4	5
6	7	8	9	10	11	12
13	14	15	16	17	18	19
20	21	22	23	24	25	26
27	28	29	30	31		

AN INTRODUCTION TO BEAR COLLECTING

MY BEGINNINGS

Collecting teddy bears has been a life-long passion of mine — what began as a childhood hobby developed into a business as I got older. Through collecting I have been able to travel all over

the world and have met some of the most wonderful people — all of us sharing a love of bears.

My interest in teddies began when I was a child. It all started when my mother's own bear was passed down to

The author's mother

Grandma's bear

me. He had been dressed by her mother in a pin-stripe waistcoat with silver buttons, and thus came to be known as Grandma's bear. It was love at first sight, and we have never been parted, except for a brief interlude when he was misplaced after a house move. Eventually, we were reunited, and today he has pride of place in my own collection where he enjoys his retirement sitting in his own little chair.

Three Steiff bears, c. 1908, considered the most desirable vintage bears by many collectors, displayed with a 19th-century child's wheelbarrow

My parents taught me how much fun collecting old things could be and as a child I would accompany them on their jaunts around the country. My interest in old things continued into adulthood; I would scour junk shops as a young woman, picking up old toys, which, of course, were much cheaper then. Soon I had the basis of a collection, which inspired me to open a shop in The Lanes in Brighton. Today, I sell old and new bears and offer a repair and restoration service for those teddies in need of special attention.

WHAT TO COLLECT

Twenty-five years ago, no one could have imagined that in the not-too-distant future, their old childhood teddy bear might be a much sought-after collector's item. Countless bears were thrown out or given to jumble sales once their owners had outgrown them. But gradually, from around the late 1970's, people started to take more of an interest in old bears. Specialist fairs for old toys and dolls began to be held in London, and were very popular. Collectors started to buy bears, hunting them out from jumble- and car-boot sales. Bears were soon big news — fetching large prices at auctions. The world record auction price stands at £110,000 for a 1906 Steiff Teddy Girl, sold at Christie's in
1994. Today, there are thousands of collectors all over the world. Most towns now have a bear shop and there are specialist auctions, teddy bear fairs, magazines and even clubs that cater for the bear lover — a small list of these appear at the back.

Some people collect bears only by famous makers. Some prefer new bears in perfect condition, while others are swayed by the appeal of a well-worn teddy. There are small bears, large bears, dressed bears and undressed bears. But when would-be collectors visit my shop to seek help in buying a bear, my advice is always the same. A bear's financial value should never be the sole motivation for buying him. It must be that particular expression and charming face — the one with the special look for you — that makes you choose your bear.

NEW BEARS
Many new collectors start with a manufactured bear made by one of the well-known factories such as Steiff, Merrythought, Dean's and Hermann. Factories often make two ranges — one specifically for children, which are safe and machine-washable, and one for collectors.

Limited Edition Bears

For the collector, the factories produce limited numbered editions, sometimes to celebrate special events. For example, each year Steiff produces these limited editions, which come boxed with a numbered certificate. It is important to keep the packaging as this always adds to the value of the bear. Limited edition bears are keenly sought after by collectors as when the stock runs out the price usually increases.

Replica Bears

Some companies also make wonderful replicas of their old bears, usually in limited editions. Steiff, in particular, has done this very successfully. In 1986 they brought out a replica of Teddy Clown, which was originally produced in the mid-twenties, and comprised 10,000 pieces world-wide. Replicas give the collector the opportunity to acquire a bear that they might otherwise not have been able to afford. These bears in turn have become collector's items in their own right.

Steiff replica (left) of Steiff Dicky Bear, c. 1933

VINTAGE BEARS

As with any antique, old bears in original and perfect condition are the most desirable. However, these will also be the most expensive and hardest to find. Sometimes it is the tattered bear that collectors find most appealing. After all, bears are toys and many old bears have had much to put up with over their long lives — they may have been a child's dearest companion, been soaked with tears, or had their stuffing knocked out of them by being loved too much.

Identifying the make and date of old bears can be very difficult — even for an expert. Vintage bears are often missing their identifying labels or buttons. Make yourself as familiar as you can with the particular characteristics of the bears from the well-known manufacturers. If you are an inexperienced collector, it is worth going to a reputable dealer, who will give you a proper receipt, as well as help and advice.

If you are intent on having a collection with vintage bears, it is still possible to pick up some from the sixties and seventies at reasonable prices. English bears from the well-known factories such as Chiltern and Chad Valley are much sought after. The mohair used was of such good quality that many of the bears have survived in wonderful condition.

Bears in need of restoration

Repairing and Restoration
There is a world of difference between restoration and repairing. Repairing is simply mending seams and patching tears, whereas restoration entails returning a bear, as nearly as possible, to his original state, which can at times be quite a challenge.

Many old bears have suffered some sort of damage over the years — thrown in an attic they may have collected dust, been attacked by moths or, stored in a damp cupboard, will have become mildewed. Some may just have suffered the wear and tear of being a child's most beloved companion.

Group of English bears from the 1950's, restored to their former glory

People mistakenly believe that repairing or restoring a bear will adversely affect his value, but as long as the work is done sensitively, using the appropriate material, it will help the bear to last longer and may even add to his value. No bear will gain in value if he is left dirty with his stuffing spilling out! I believe a small hole mended now will prevent a larger hole in the future.

The first stage in restoring a bear is to identify his original maker. Then, you can refer to the many excellent books available, which will help you to use the correct fabric when mending paws, to replace the nose stitching and claws as they would have been, and very importantly to fit the right eyes. The original eyes of many old bears have been removed because their wire fixings were considered unsafe by parents. They were often replaced with button eyes or sewed-on eyes using wool.

It is very much more difficult to restore a bear with no identification, but it is possible to look for the old stitch marks and follow them when replacing the nose and claws. There may also be some fabric left on the paws that will give you a clue as to what the original was like. All this detective work can be quite fascinating and your bear will be much happier.

Almost all the bears I see are in need of cleaning. Dust settles onto the mohair over the years, which if allowed to remain, results in the fabric rotting. It is important to clean your bear, but never do this without taking advice.

For difficult restoration, especially on valuable old bears, there are professional bear restorers, as well as doll and bear hospitals across the country. A small list appears at the back of the book.

Documentation
When buying an old bear, try to find out as much as possible about his history. Stories about a bear's past are often handed down from generation to generation. You may be able to find out where and when he was bought, whether he has a name or any stories associated with him. You may even be lucky enough to be given a photograph of the bear with his original owner. I have two bears in my collection that were given to their owners when they were very young and were still with them when they died. A bear's history and photographs can greatly add to his desirability and value.

This photograph from the early part of this century can help
document the bear's history

Original Clothing
A specialist area of collecting, and a
particular interest of mine, is finding
old bears in their original clothing.
Dressed bears add great variety to a
collection, but do expect to pay
more for them as they are
quite rare.

Steiff bear, c. 1908, wearing
original hand-made clothes.

In the early part of this century,
young girls were taught the art
of sewing, knitting and

sometimes crocheting. This was a regular part of their education, and they often practised on their dolls and teddies. With diligent hunting it is possible to track down these bears dressed in the wonderful handiwork of their young owners — or sometimes their owners' mothers. Larger bears were often dressed in the family baby clothes.

The factories also sometimes dressed their bears. For example, the first Chiltern bear ever made, Master Teddy, was dressed in felt trousers and a shirt. Much later, in the 1950's, Schuco made

Chiltern Master Teddy, c. 1915 (right), in his original factory-made clothes with a Steiff bear, c. 1910, dressed in clothes made by his young owner

dressed bears. This was after the war, when mohair was in short supply; beneath the clothing the body was made of cotton.

If the clothes are removable, it is instructive to see the bear's original colour and condition, where he has been protected. Even if the bear is cleaned, he will still keep the two colours as it is impossible to restore colour to faded mohair.

ARTIST BEARS

Today there are hundreds of artist bear makers around the world. These are people who design and make all their own bears. The designs are usually made in small numbers and are signed on a label by the artists. There is great scope for collecting in the area, as the bears come in all price ranges with bears to match everyone's taste — dressed and undressed, fanciful or lifelike. Many of the artists are well known and have waiting lists for their bears, often running into several months, or even longer. Expect to pay more for the more popular artists. These bears should not be given to small children as they do not conform to safety regulations.

MINIATURE BEARS

Another interesting area for the collector is miniature bears. These cross over several categories. Schuco introduced their range of miniature bears in Germany in the 1920's, and continued until the seventies. These often had novelty elements. One design was actually a perfume bottle, which was opened by removing the bear's head to reveal a glass stopper. Another design took the shape of a powder compact, where the body of the bear concealed a lipstick, the powder and sometimes even a tiny mirror.

Miniature bears by Goody Two Shoes with hand-made accessories

There are vintage miniature bears whose makers will never be known, but are none the less very collectable. An example of these are the delightful Soldier Bears. These were made during World War I, and were used by the soldiers as mascots. They were often tucked into their top pockets and as a result many survive today without their nose stitching or their ears, which are simply pieces of wire covered in mohair set into the head. I like to think these mascots brought their owners luck. I have one soldier bear called Wilf. He belonged to a World War I pilot who lived to the ripe old age of eighty-five.

There are also many talented artists working today who specialise in making miniature bears. Their skill, ingenuity and inventiveness is amazing. Sometimes these tiny bears carry even smaller bears, rabbits, gollies or other accessories. They are often dressed in exquisitely made clothes. It is no wonder that these bears are in such demand.

DISPLAYING BEARS

Once you have started a collection, you must think of the best way of displaying your bears, showing them to their advantage. A good way to do this, as well as adding interest to and expanding your collection, is to display the bears

Paper bear, 1920's

Early teddy bear book

with bear memorabilia. This can be done very cheaply, for example, with postcards and biscuit tins, or more expensively, with silverware, such as children's rattles —

so price need not be a major consideration. Children's books can also show off the collection, and toys can be placed among the bears to great effect.

I always feel bears look very sad sitting alone, so I prefer to give them other toys and books to play with and often sit them on small chairs or in prams and old cots.

Old bears displayed with newer models, bears of varying sizes and from different factories, bears dressed and undressed — they are all possibilities. Allow your imagination full rein.

BUILDING YOUR COLLECTION

Pair of loveable collectable bears, 1950's, unknown maker

Searching for that special bear is a fascinating pastime. Visit the teddy bear shows, where you will find bears old and new, the specialist shops and the teddy bear auctions. This will give you the opportunity to see and to handle a wide variety of bears.

As you gain experience you may find your taste changes. Many people have begun by buying new bears and then started to expand their collection to include old bears, perhaps specialising in a specific manufacturer's ranges, or a certain period, or bears from one particular country.

If you have decided to specialise, try to buy the very best you can afford in that area. Even so, you will probably find that you fall in love with a bear that doesn't fit your criteria. If so, buy him! Collecting is about much more than profit — a good collection must give enjoyment. I personally like all my old teddies with their mellow and slightly shabby charm as well as my jaunty new bears with their delightful bright faces. Each and every one gives me great happiness.

DECEMBER 1998/JANUARY 1999

MONDAY 28

HOLIDAY, UK

TUESDAY 29

WEDNESDAY 30

THURSDAY 31

FRIDAY 1

NEW YEAR'S DAY

SATURDAY 2

SUNDAY 3

Roosevelt bear, c. 1904 and Steiff bear, c. 1910

The bear on the right is a 13 inch (33 cm) Steiff, known as 'Teddy Loring'. Theodore Roosevelt presented him to John Alden Loring, who had accompanied the President on safari to Africa. On the left is a 10 inch (25 cm) Ideal bear. This type of bear was thrown from the back of Roosevelt's presidential campaign train in the summer of 1904. Attached to 'Teddy Loring' is a lapel pin bear, another rare item from the 1904 presidential campaign. Although not an actual teddy, he and the Ideal bear can claim to be the very first representations of 'Teddy's bear' prior to the name being shortened to teddy bear.

JANUARY 1999

MONDAY 4

HOLIDAY, SCOTLAND

TUESDAY 5

WEDNESDAY 6

THURSDAY 7

FRIDAY 8

SATURDAY 9

SUNDAY 10

JANUARY 1999

MONDAY 11

TUESDAY 12

WEDNESDAY 13

THURSDAY 14

FRIDAY 15

SATURDAY 16

SUNDAY 17

MONDAY 18

TUESDAY 19

WEDNESDAY 20

IDEAL BEAR, C. 1904
The bear here is pictured with an original Clifford Berryman illustration. Berryman, a political cartoonist of the day, was responsible for the famous drawing of Roosevelt refusing to shoot a bear. Berryman continued to draw his bears with distinctive googly eyes for many years — a feature of the early Ideal bears.

IDEAL BEAR, c. 1910
The Ideal Toy Company was founded in 1902 by Rose and Morris Michtom, two Russian émigrés to the US. It took their ingenuity to transform the bear depicted in the Berryman cartoon into a soft toy.

THURSDAY 21

FRIDAY 22

SATURDAY 23

SUNDAY 24

JANUARY 1999

MONDAY 25

TUESDAY 26

AUSTRALIA DAY, AUSTRALIA

WEDNESDAY 27

THURSDAY 28

FRIDAY 29

SATURDAY 30

SUNDAY 31

FEBRUARY 1999

MONDAY 1

TUESDAY 2

WEDNESDAY 3

THURSDAY 4

FRIDAY 5

SATURDAY 6

WAITANGI DAY, NEW ZEALAND

SUNDAY 7

FEBRUARY 1999

MONDAY 8

TUESDAY 9

WEDNESDAY 10

THURSDAY 11

FRIDAY 12

SATURDAY 13

SUNDAY 14

STEIFF BEAR, c. 1905

Margarete Steiff, who was born in Giengen, Germany in 1847, founded the world-famous company that still bears her name, in 1893. This is a rare early Steiff. He has a cone-shaped nose, which gives him his distinctive look. He has long arms, black button eyes and ears set wide apart on his head, which are all characteristics of early Steiffs.

FEBRUARY 1999

MONDAY 15

TUESDAY 16

WEDNESDAY 17

THURSDAY 18

FRIDAY 19

SATURDAY 20

SUNDAY 21

FEBRUARY 1999

MONDAY 22

TUESDAY 23

WEDNESDAY 24

THURSDAY 25

FRIDAY 26

SATURDAY 27

SUNDAY 28

MARCH 1999

MONDAY 1

TUESDAY 2

WEDNESDAY 3

THURSDAY 4

FRIDAY 5

SATURDAY 6

SUNDAY 7

MERRYTHOUGHT BEARS, c. 1935

W. G. Holmes and G. H. Laxton founded Merrythought in 1930 in Ironbridge, Shropshire. Both bears have a celluloid button in their ear, and the bear on the left has an embossed label on his foot. They both have glass eyes and vertically stitched noses with dropped ends.

MARCH 1999

MONDAY 8

TUESDAY 9

WEDNESDAY 10

THURSDAY 11

FRIDAY 12

SATURDAY 13

SUNDAY 14

MARCH 1999

MONDAY 15

TUESDAY 16

WEDNESDAY 17

ST PATRICK'S DAY, NORTHERN IRELAND

THURSDAY 18

FRIDAY 19

SATURDAY 20

SUNDAY 21

MARCH 1999

MONDAY 22

TUESDAY 23

WEDNESDAY 24

STEIFF BEAR, c. 1907
This handsome 25 inch (64 cm) bear has long shaggy mohair. He retains the button in his ear. These were often lost as children pulled them out.

STEIFF CAT, c. 1950
Steiff produced toys other than
bears. This cat is fully jointed
so can adopt many poses.

THURSDAY 25

FRIDAY 26

SATURDAY 27

SUNDAY 28

MARCH/APRIL 1999

MONDAY 29

TUESDAY 30

WEDNESDAY 31

THURSDAY 1

FRIDAY 2

GOOD FRIDAY

SATURDAY 3

SUNDAY 4

EASTER DAY

APRIL 1999

MONDAY 5

HOLIDAY, UK (EXCEPT SCOTLAND), NEW ZEALAND AND CANADA

TUESDAY 6

WEDNESDAY 7

THURSDAY 8

FRIDAY 9

SATURDAY 10

SUNDAY 11

FARNELL BEAR, c. 1930

J. K. Farnell was founded in London in 1897. Farnell bears are the most collectable of the English bears and are very hard to come by. This is a 28 inch (71 cm) *Alpha*, a range first produced by the factory in the twenties. He has long curling mohair and large glass eyes. He is in mint condition.

APRIL 1999

MONDAY 12

TUESDAY 13

WEDNESDAY 14

THURSDAY 15

FRIDAY 16

SATURDAY 17

SUNDAY 18

APRIL 1999

MONDAY 19

TUESDAY 20

WEDNESDAY 21

THURSDAY 22

FRIDAY 23

SATURDAY 24

SUNDAY 25

ANZAC DAY, AUSTRALIA AND NEW ZEALAND

APRIL/MAY 1999

MONDAY 26

TUESDAY 27

WEDNESDAY 28

THURSDAY 29

FRIDAY 30

SATURDAY 1

SUNDAY 2

MAY 1999

MONDAY 3

HOLIDAY, UK

TUESDAY 4

WEDNESDAY 5

THURSDAY 6

FRIDAY 7

SATURDAY 8

SUNDAY 9

CHAD VALLEY BEARS, 1930's

Chad Valley developed out of a successful stationery and bookbinding business founded in 1823, known as Johnson Bros. In 1897, the company moved from Birmingham to Harborne on the Chad River, adding the Wrenkin Toy Factory to the business. In 1919, the company changed its name to Chad Valley. Both these bears have large cupped ears and shaved muzzles. Their vertically stitched triangular noses are typical of early Chads. The bear on the right has the red-and-white identifying label on his foot.

MAY 1999

MONDAY 10

TUESDAY 11

WEDNESDAY 12

THURSDAY 13

FRIDAY 14

SATURDAY 15

SUNDAY 16

MAY 1999

MONDAY 17

TUESDAY 18

WEDNESDAY 19

THURSDAY 20

FRIDAY 21

SATURDAY 22

SUNDAY 23

MONDAY 24

VICTORIA DAY, CANADA

TUESDAY 25

WEDNESDAY 26

FARNELL BEARS, 1920's
The smallest bear has black button eyes, which is a common feature of Farnells under 16 inches (41 cm), in contrast to the clear glass eyes of the larger bears. The two larger bears have the classic Farnell webbed stitching on their paws.

MAY 1999

MERRYTHOUGHT BEARS, c. 1935 AND 1960'S
The bear in the centre, from the thirties, is flanked by bears belonging to the popular Cheeky range, first produced in 1957. Cheekies have large domed heads, bells in their ears, prominent noses and wide-stitched smiles.

THURSDAY 27

FRIDAY 28

SATURDAY 29

SUNDAY 30

MAY/JUNE 1999

MONDAY 31

HOLIDAY, UK

TUESDAY 1

WEDNESDAY 2

THURSDAY 3

FRIDAY 4

SATURDAY 5

SUNDAY 6

JUNE 1999

MONDAY 7

THE QUEEN'S BIRTHDAY, NEW ZEALAND

TUESDAY 8

WEDNESDAY 9

THURSDAY 10

FRIDAY 11

SATURDAY 12

SUNDAY 13

JUNE 1999

MONDAY 14

TUESDAY 15

WEDNESDAY 16

THURSDAY 17

FRIDAY 18

SATURDAY 19

SUNDAY 20

SCHUCO PANDA, 1950'S AND SCHUCO BELLHOP MONKEY, 1920'S
Schuco was the trademark of Schreyer & Co. founded in 1912 and based in Nuremberg. The panda and the monkey are Yes/No toys — by moving their tails, their heads can go up and down and side to side. These are examples of the novelty items which were a hallmark of the company. Schuco also produced bellhop bears, which are very rare.

JUNE 1999

MONDAY 21

TUESDAY 22

WEDNESDAY 23

THURSDAY 24

FRIDAY 25

SATURDAY 26

SUNDAY 27

JUNE/JULY 1999

MONDAY 28

TUESDAY 29

WEDNESDAY 30

THURSDAY 1

CANADA DAY, CANADA

FRIDAY 2

SATURDAY 3

SUNDAY 4

JULY 1999

MONDAY 5

TUESDAY 6

WEDNESDAY 7

THURSDAY 8

FRIDAY 9

SATURDAY 10

SUNDAY 11

BING BEARS, c. 1908 AND c. 1925

Gebrüder Bing, founded in 1863, was based in Nuremberg, and specialised in producing mechanical boats, trains and cars before concentrating on bears. These bears, although both from the same factory, are very different. The smaller bear is the earlier one. He has a wide head with small ears set at the corners, black button eyes and his oval feet have cardboard inserts. The later bear has glass eyes and a large head with a long smiling mouth that goes along the length of his muzzle.

JULY 1999

MONDAY 12

BATTLE OF THE BOYNE, NORTHERN IRELAND

TUESDAY 13

WEDNESDAY 14

THURSDAY 15

FRIDAY 16

SATURDAY 17

SUNDAY 18

JULY 1999

MONDAY 19

TUESDAY 20

WEDNESDAY 21

THURSDAY 22

FRIDAY 23

SATURDAY 24

SUNDAY 25

JULY 1999

MONDAY 26

TUESDAY 27

WEDNESDAY 28

CHAD VALLEY BEAR, C. 1950
This bear is in mint condition. He was never played with by his young owner who preferred dolls, and so was packed away in a cupboard.

JULY/AUGUST 1999

BING BEAR, c. 1925
This magnificent bear is 28 inches
(71 cm) and has a pronounced hump.
He is very chubby, with large oval feet
and felt paw pads. He is a rare colour;
he once had brown tipping but is now a
beautiful blond.

THURSDAY 29

FRIDAY 30

SATURDAY 31

SUNDAY 1

AUGUST 1999

MONDAY 2

HOLIDAY, SCOTLAND

TUESDAY 3

WEDNESDAY 4

THURSDAY 5

FRIDAY 6

SATURDAY 7

SUNDAY 8

AUGUST 1999

MONDAY 9

TUESDAY 10

WEDNESDAY 11

THURSDAY 12

FRIDAY 13

SATURDAY 14

SUNDAY 15

AUGUST 1999

MONDAY 16

TUESDAY 17

WEDNESDAY 18

THURSDAY 19

FRIDAY 20

SATURDAY 21

SUNDAY 22

CHILTERN BEAR, 1930's

The toy company H. G. Stone was founded in 1920 by Leon Rees and Harry Stone. Its factory was based in Chesham in the Chiltern Hills and the company's trademark was Chiltern Toys. The bear above is 28 inches (71 cm), has velvet paw pads and a vertically stitched nose, with two long ends. He is stuffed with kapok, so is very light and easy for a child to carry around. With him is an Edwardian collar box, hand painted, with a golliwog and teddy, by the well-known Australian artist Kathy Karas.

AUGUST 1999

MONDAY 23

TUESDAY 24

WEDNESDAY 25

THURSDAY 26

FRIDAY 27

SATURDAY 28

SUNDAY 29

AUGUST/SEPTEMBER 1999

MONDAY 30

TUESDAY 31

WEDNESDAY 1

THURSDAY 2

FRIDAY 3

SATURDAY 4

SUNDAY 5

SEPTEMBER 1999

MONDAY 6

LABOUR DAY, CANADA

TUESDAY 7

WEDNESDAY 8

THURSDAY 9

FRIDAY 10

SATURDAY 11

SUNDAY 12

MAKE UNKNOWN, c. 1910

This early German bear was possibly made by Strunz, a company which copied Steiff
bears. He is 25 inches (64 cm) and has black button eyes. When he was being restored
it was discovered that he had been stuffed with the Birmingham Gazette from 1918.

SEPTEMBER 1999

MONDAY 13

TUESDAY 14

WEDNESDAY 15

THURSDAY 16

FRIDAY 17

SATURDAY 18

SUNDAY 19

SEPTEMBER 1999

MONDAY 20

TUESDAY 21

WEDNESDAY 22

THURSDAY 23

FRIDAY 24

SATURDAY 25

SUNDAY 26

SEPTEMBER 1999

MONDAY 27

TUESDAY 28

WEDNESDAY 29

ALLY BEAR, c. 1915 AND MAKE
UNKNOWN, c. 1915

*The larger bear is an Ally bear. These military
bears, dressed in the uniforms of the allied forces,
were manufactured by the London-based company
Harwin & Co. during the First World War. The
smaller bear, from the same period, is dressed in
the original clothes of the time.*

STEIFF BEARS,
c. 1907-1910

*Red felt shows through the pads of
the largest bear, which marks him as
an early Steiff. The bear in the
jumper has a side squeaker, which
dates him from around 1907. The
little white bear has no paw pads —
this is typical of the smallest-sized
Steiffs.*

THURSDAY 30

FRIDAY 1

SATURDAY 2

SUNDAY 3

OCTOBER 1999

MONDAY 4

TUESDAY 5

WEDNESDAY 6

THURSDAY 7

FRIDAY 8

SATURDAY 9

SUNDAY 10

OCTOBER 1999

MONDAY 11

THANKSGIVING DAY, CANADA

TUESDAY 12

WEDNESDAY 13

THURSDAY 14

FRIDAY 15

SATURDAY 16

SUNDAY 17

STEIFF BEAR, c. 1908 AND FARNELL BEAR, c. 1914
The larger bear, called 'Morris', is a Steiff. He has a centre seam. He is seated with
'Midge', a Farnell. Both are dressed in contemporary clothing of the day. The toy
wood boat is from Germany, c. 1900.

OCTOBER 1999

MONDAY 18

TUESDAY 19

WEDNESDAY 20

THURSDAY 21

FRIDAY 22

SATURDAY 23

SUNDAY 24

OCTOBER 1999

MONDAY 25

LABOUR DAY, NEW ZEALAND

TUESDAY 26

WEDNESDAY 27

THURSDAY 28

FRIDAY 29

SATURDAY 30

SUNDAY 31

NOVEMBER 1999

MONDAY 1

TUESDAY 2

WEDNESDAY 3

THURSDAY 4

FRIDAY 5

SATURDAY 6

SUNDAY 7

NOVEMBER 1999

MONDAY 8

TUESDAY 9

WEDNESDAY 10

THURSDAY 11

REMEMBRANCE DAY, CANADA

FRIDAY 12

SATURDAY 13

SUNDAY 14

SCHUCO BEAR, 1950'S AND SCHUCO ORANG-UTAN, 1920'S

The bear and the orang-utan are both Yes/No toys. The bear is 10 inches (25 cm), has glass eyes and is made of gold mohair. His broad paws with pads facing downward are typical of this type. The orang-utan is very rare.

NOVEMBER 1999

MONDAY 15

TUESDAY 16

WEDNESDAY 17

THURSDAY 18

FRIDAY 19

SATURDAY 20

SUNDAY 21

NOVEMBER 1999

MONDAY 22

TUESDAY 23

WEDNESDAY 24

THURSDAY 25

FRIDAY 26

SATURDAY 27

SUNDAY 28

MONDAY 29

TUESDAY 30

WEDNESDAY 1

CHILTERN BEAR AND
CHILTERN RABBIT,
1930'S AND STEIFF
DUCK, 1950'S
*This photograph shows the
diversity of both Chiltern's and
Steiff's output. The Chiltern
toys are known as Skater Bear
and Skater Rabbit. They are
both made of artificial silk
plush and are in excellent
condition. The bear has a label
on her foot, which helps date
her from the early thirties.*

CHILTERN BEARS, C. 1950 AND 1930'S
Both bears belong to the Hugmee
range. The larger bar was produced
after the Second World War to a new
pattern, using less material. He has the
typical Chiltern claw stitching – two
claws on either side sewn onto rexine
paw pads. The smaller, earlier bear has
a longer nose, glass eyes and cotton paw
pads.

THURSDAY 2

FRIDAY 3

SATURDAY 4

SUNDAY 5

DECEMBER 1999

MONDAY 6

TUESDAY 7

WEDNESDAY 8

THURSDAY 9

FRIDAY 10

SATURDAY 11

SUNDAY 12

DECEMBER 1999

MONDAY 13

TUESDAY 14

WEDNESDAY 15

THURSDAY 16

FRIDAY 17

SATURDAY 18

SUNDAY 19

MUSICAL BEARS, c. 1925

These two beautiful German musical clown bears are in mint condition. The music is made by squeezing their stomachs. This is known as a bellows movement. The bear on the left has the bat-wing nose typical of Helvetic bears. The bear on the right has horizontal nose stitching and large eyes. He was made by the firm Jopi, the trade name of Joseph Pitterman of Nuremberg.

DECEMBER 1999

MONDAY 20

TUESDAY 21

WEDNESDAY 22

THURSDAY 23

FRIDAY 24

SATURDAY 25

CHRISTMAS DAY

SUNDAY 26

BOXING DAY

DECEMBER 1999/JANUARY 2000

MONDAY 27

HOLIDAY, UK

TUESDAY 28

HOLIDAY, UK

WEDNESDAY 29

THURSDAY 30

FRIDAY 31

SATURDAY 1

NEW YEAR'S DAY

SUNDAY 2

JANUARY 2000

MONDAY 3

HOLIDAY, UK

TUESDAY 4

HOLIDAY, SCOTLAND

WEDNESDAY 5

THURSDAY 6

FRIDAY 7

SATURDAY 8

SUNDAY 9

JANUARY 2000

MONDAY 10

TUESDAY 11

WEDNESDAY 12

FARNELL BEARS,
1950'S AND MAKE
UNKNOWN C. 1960
The blue bear (on the left),
make unknown, is made of
plush cotton. He is seated with
two Farnells. Their short limbs
are typical of the the post
World War II period. The
smaller bear has a musical
movement in his body.

CHAD VALLEY BEAR, c. 1930
AND CHILTERN BEAR, c. 1950
The Chiltern is made of gold mohair and has the remains of his label on his right foot. He has a stitched shield shaped nose. The Chad Valley bear, made of red cotton plush is very rare. He has a large nose, typical of his make, and a celluloid button in his ear. The toy horse is German from around 1900.

THURSDAY 13

FRIDAY 14

SATURDAY 15

SUNDAY 16

JANUARY 2000

Monday 17

Tuesday 18

Wednesday 19

Thursday 20

Friday 21

Saturday 22

Sunday 23

JANUARY 2000

MONDAY 24

TUESDAY 25

WEDNESDAY 26

AUSTRALIA DAY, AUSTRALIA

THURSDAY 27

FRIDAY 28

SATURDAY 29

SUNDAY 30

IDENTIFYING OLD BEARS

BUTTONS AND LABELS

Identification of old bears can be very difficult and often frustrating, even for the experienced collector. Buttons and labels which carry the manufacturer's name or have a design or logo specific to one company, have been used since the early part of the century: these are a guide to a bear's make, and the style and wording on buttons and labels, which changed through the years, a clue to dating.

There are drawbacks, however, to relying solely on these items for identification and dating. One difficulty is that many old bears no longer have their original buttons and labels, which were easily removed by their young owners: if you find an old teddy still in possession of a paper swing label, chances are he was never played with. Another problem is that buttons can be forged: the addition of a metal button, which has been distressed to look old and therefore original, is a device used by the unscrupulous.

So although it is best to make yourself as familiar as possible with the styles of the different manufacturers, buttons and labels are the necessary starting point for identification. Just when you think you have a good grasp of the style of the different makers, a bear turns up without any labels or buttons that is impossible to identify. You may be able to hazard a guess at his age by looking at the length of his arms or nose; you might even guess his country of origin. But nothing is certain unless you can find a similar bear that still has his identifying button or label. The photographs here show the range of these items.

 *Steiff Buttons* These were first introduced in 1904-1905. They had an elephant with a curved trunk in the shape of an S, and were sewn into the bear's ear. The words 'button in the ear' became the Steiff trademark. At the same time, some blank buttons were also in use, and these

appear sporadically even later. After 1905, the word 'Steiff' was printed in capital letters on the button, with the tail of the last F underscoring the whole word. This design was used until 1950 when a printed button with 'Steiff' written on it, without the underscoring, was introduced. Steiff bears also have labels, which have changed through the years.

Bing Buttons Early Bing bears had a metal arrow in their right ear. This was replaced in 1909 by a button incised with the letters G.B.N. placed under the arm. This was used until 1919, when a button with the initials B.W. on the right arm was introduced.

Chad Valley Labels From the 1930's Chad Valley attached a white embroidered label to the foot of their bears. In 1938, they were granted a Royal Warrant, and from then their labels read 'Toymakers to Her Majesty the Queen'. These words changed in 1953 after the coronation, when the Queen became the Queen Mother. Chad Valley bears also had labels sewn in their side seam, as well as paper swing labels, which have mostly disappeared. Buttons were used by Chad Valley as early as 1923.

Chiltern Labels Chilterns had sewn-on labels as well as swing paper labels. The early labels read 'Chiltern Toys Made in England'. The first printed label on the foot is from the 1940's.

Merrythought Labels The first embroidered labels had the words 'Merrythought Hygienic Toys England'. From 1945-1956 a printed label, with the same words, was introduced. From 1957-1991 the printed label said 'Merrythought Ironbridge Shrops'.

USEFUL DATES AND ADDRESSES

PUBLICATIONS

Bear Collector
(published 4 times a year)
Ashdown Publishing, Avalon Court,
Star Road, Partridge Green,
West Sussex, RH13 8RY
Tel: (01403) 711511

The International Teddy Bear Club Magazine
(published 12 times a year)
Castle House, 97 High Street,
Colchester, Essex CO1 1TH
Tel: (01206) 578690

Teddy Bear and Friends
(published 6 times a year)
6405 Flank Drive, Harrisburg
PA 17112, USA
Tel: 717. 657. 9555

Teddy Bear Review
(published 6 times a year)
170 Fifth Avenue, New York
NY 10010, USA
Tel: 212. 989. 8700

The Teddy Bear Times
(published 12 times a year)
see Bear Collector

The UK Teddy Bear Guide
(published yearly)
Hugglets
P.O. Box 290, Brighton BN2 1DR
Tel: (01273) 697974

MUSEUMS

Please check opening times before travelling.

The Bear Museum
38 Dragon Street, Petersfield, Hants GU31 4JJ
Tel: (01730) 265108

The Bethnal Green Museum of Childhood
Cambridge Heath Road, London E2 9PA
Tel: (0181) 983 5200

The Broadway Teddy Bear Museum
76 High Street, Broadway, Worcs WR12 7AJ
Tel: (01386) 858323

Steiff Museum, Margarete Steiff GmbH
Alleenstr. 2, D-89537 Giengen (Brenz)
Germany
Tel: ring Steiff Club

Teddy Bear Museum of Naples
2511 Pine Ridge Road, Naples
Florida 34109, USA
Tel: 941. 598. 2711

Teddy Melrose
Scotland's Teddy Bear Museum
High Street, Melrose, Scotland TD6 9PA
Tel: (01896) 822464

Toy & Teddy Bear Museum
373 Clifton Drive North, St Anne's
Lancs FY8 2PA
Tel: (01253) 713705

BEAR REPAIRS

The author cannot accept responsibility for
any repairs undertaken – except her own.

Brian Beacock
76 Shortwood Avenue, Staines
Middlesex TW18 4JL
Tel: (01784) 451631

The Midland Dolls' Hospital and Bear Clinic
48 Doxey, Stafford ST16 1EB
Tel: (01785) 241726

Sue Pearson, 13 1/2 Prince Albert Street
The Lanes, Brighton BN1 1HE
Tel: (01273) 329247

TEDDY BEAR CLUBS

Bear Talk Club, Judy Thomas
c/o Eversley Bears, 37 Grove Road
Stratford-upon-Avon, Warwicks
Tel: (01789) 292334

British Bear Club
Avalon Court, Star Road, Partridge Green,
West Sussex RH13 8RY
Tel: (01403) 711511

British Teddy Bear Association
PO Box 290, Brighton BN2 lDR
Tel: (01273) 697974

Steiff Club, Margarete Steiff GmbH
Alleenstr. 2, D-89537 Giengen (Brenz)
Germany
Tel: 7322. 131. 452

BEAR FAIRS 1999

Please confirm event before travelling.

FEBRUARY

Winter BearFest, Kensington Town Hall
London W8
Organisers: Hugglets
PO Box 290, Brighton, BN2 lDR
Tel: (01273) 697974

MARCH

Leeds Doll & Teddy Fair, Pudsey Civic Hall
Leeds, Yorks
Organisers: Liz and David Bonner
Tel: (0191) 455 2463/424 0400

APRIL

The Rochester Teddy Bear Fair
The Rigging House, Chatham Historic
Dockyard, Chatham, Kent
Organisers: Michelle and Carol Chambers
Tel: (01634) 831615

The Big Teddy Bear Show
Business Design Centre, Islington Green
London N1
Organisers: The Teddy Bear Times
Avalon Court, Star Road, Partridge Green
West Sussex, RH13 8RY
Tel: (01403) 711511

MAY

Tyneside Doll & Teddy Fair
Gateshead Civic Centre, Regent Street
Gateshead, Tyne-and-Wear
Organisers: Liz and David Bonner, see March

Festival of Artist Bears, Kensington Town
Hall, London W8
Organisers: Hugglets, see February

AUGUST

Teddies '99 Festival, Kensington Town Hall,
London W8
Organisers: Hugglets, see February

Tyneside Doll & Teddy Fair, *see May*

OCTOBER

Leeds Doll & Teddy Fair, *see March*

The Rochester Teddy Bear Fair, *see April*

NOVEMBER

Teddy Bear Celebration
Organisers: Hugglets, see February

DECEMBER

British Bear Fair, Hove Town Hall
Hove, East Sussex
Organisers: The Teddy Bear Times, see April

AUCTIONS

The major auction houses – Christie's,
Sotheby's and Bonhams – hold regular sales
of teddy bears, dolls and soft toys, and will
give free evaluations. In 1993 Christie's
held the first auction devoted exclusively to
bears.

Christie's
85 Old Brompton Road, London SW7 3LD
Contact: Leyla Maniera
Tel: (0171) 581 7611

Sotheby's
34 New Bond Street, London WlA 2AA
Contact: Bunny Campione
Tel: (0171) 493 8080

Bonhams
65-69 Lots Road, London SW10 ORN
Contact: Leigh Gotch
Tel: (0171) 393 3900

ACKNOWLEDGEMENTS AND PHOTOGRAPH CREDITS

The author would like to thank the Design House, Steyning, West Sussex and Mulberry at Home for the use of their fabrics.

All bears and related bear objects courtesy of the author and photographs by *Roddy Paine* with the following exceptions:

Guy Ryecart: Introduction – Steiff replica and Dicky Bear; Chiltern Master Teddy; Jan. 21-23; Feb. 8-14; May 24-30; Sept. 27-Oct. 3; Nov. 29-Dec. 5; Identifying Old Bears; and below

Michael Pearson: Introduction – Grandma's bear, Bears in need of restoration; Miniature bears by Goody Two Shoes; Paper bear; Early teddy book; Unknown collectable bears

Photographer unknown: Introduction – The author's mother; Steiff label; Early photograph; *Fiona Pragoff*; Endpapers

FARNELL BEAR, 1920's

STEIFF BEAR, c. 1908

MAKE UNKNOWN (Possibly American)

MAKE UNKNOWN, c. 1935

MERRYTHOUGHT BEAR, c. 1936

MAKE UNKNOWN (Possibly German), c. 1912